Who Lives Here?

by June Melser

Who lives here?

One snake.

2

Who lives here?

Two lizards.

Who lives here?

Three birds.

Who lives here?

One kangaroo?

No. Two kangaroos?

No. Three kangaroos
live here.